THE RAFT

AND

SOCRATES ASKS WHY

In The Cornerstones, *the first of these Conversations, the idea was put forward that there is, in the United Nations, sufficient community of interest to warrant the establishment, by Great Britain, China, the United States, and Russia, of a rule of world-wide law. Given the vision, given courage, it could be done. . . . Then in* The Raft, *the second Conversation, the state of Britain is considered. Are the people of Britain capable of serving the new world, of writing with honour a new chapter of history ? The answer, conclusively, is Yes. . . . But Socrates, in the third of the pieces, has still to be satisfied that the Allies are truly conscious of their purpose. A four-fold rule of law is not enough : the peace within that rule must not be an idle peace, but creative. If that is not explicitly our intention and desire, then why are we fighting ?*

NOTE.—The Cornerstones *was published in December of last year, and twice broadcast early in this.* The Raft *was broadcast in August, and* Socrates Asks Why *in early October 1942.*

THE RAFT

and

SOCRATES ASKS WHY

Two Conversations

by

ERIC LINKLATER

LONDON
MACMILLAN & CO. LTD
1942

PRINTED IN GREAT BRITAIN
BY R. & R. CLARK, LIMITED, EDINBURGH

TO

JAMES BRIDIE

A CIVILISED MAN

THE RAFT

A raft is floating on the Atlantic. The long swell lifts it, raising first one corner so that it lies steeply tilted, and the opposite corner dips into the sea. The water, with a flourish of white, runs along its lower side. The bodies on the raft begin to roll downhill, but they have been tied to the planking, and the ropes halt their movement abruptly. Then the raft is tilted in the opposite direction, and again the bodies move a little way, uneasily.

The Atlantic is almost black, and the swell is ribbed with a fresh wind, here and there white-bearded. The sky hangs low in dull and formless clouds. A shower of rain, swift and savage, runs over the sea and striking hard upon the raft, rebounds, from planking and bodies, in small crystal fountains. There is a break in the clouds, and the view enlarges. On the desolate circle of ocean there is nothing to be seen but the raft. It rises on a swell, and disappears into a darker gulf.

There are six bodies on it. Two of them, on the

sleeves of their sodden jackets, wear tarnished gold braid. One of them, very young, his lank hair a light gold, is a LIEUTENANT *in the Royal Naval Volunteer Reserve. The other, also young but dark and thick-set, was* SECOND MATE *of the ship that has been torpedoed. Between them lies the tall figure of a* STOKER. *He is a very big man with enormous feet. He has tied a grey blanket round his shoulders, but one arm, thickly muscled, is naked to the wind.*

On the other side of the raft are a WIRELESS OPERATOR, *a* GUNNER, *and a* PASSENGER. *The first, lightly built with sharp features, wears a black oilskin lashed tightly round his thin body. The* GUNNER, *in a dufflecoat and soldier's khaki trousers, is the survivor of the crew of a twin-Lewis, the ship's anti-aircraft armament. The* PASSENGER, *the oldest man there, in his middle forties, is hooded in a tartan travelling-rug buttoned into a dark civilian greatcoat.*

Between these six men, so different in many ways, there is one close resemblance. They are in the border-land between life and death, and they wear a look of peace. Their minds have been released from pain, and their thoughts make conversation.

2

PASSENGER

I felt the rain. I don't think I shall feel anything more.

WIRELESS OPERATOR

I felt nothing.

GUNNER

Nor I.

LIEUTENANT

Yes, it was rain. The last time I sailed a race, in the summer before the war, there was a rain-squall like that as we rounded the buoy for the last leg to windward. A summer squall, but fierce and blinding. I was third across the line, but I won on handicap.

STOKER

It was raining when I left Liverpool. My wife didn't want me to go back to sea. She said : 'You've been bombed, and torpedoed, and wrecked ashore. Three ships you've lost already.

You've done your share if any man has. Stay with me now. Get a job on land.' — But she didn't make a fuss when I said no. She's a good wife, light of heart, and the child takes after her.

PASSENGER

You have been wrecked three times before this ?

STOKER

Two years ago was the first time. More than that. It was the week when the Germans bombed Rotterdam and murdered, how many thousand ? A fine port, Rotterdam. We had discharged there, and were outward bound in ballast. But a U-boat met us three hundred miles west of Land's End. I fell and burnt my shoulder getting out of the stoke-hole. We were five days in a lifeboat, nineteen of us, but the weather wasn't too bad. Then we got picked up, and I was back to sea within a fortnight.

About nine or ten months after that we went ashore somewhere in the Outer Hebrides. I forget the name of the place. We were light again, being west-bound, and a full gale was blowing into the Minch. It was a dirty night. There were more ships than one lost that night. In time of war, when all the lighthouses are dark, ships are like blind men, very subject to disaster. But some of us got ashore, over rocks that were sharp as a razor where they weren't slippery with seaweed. And a few cuts don't take long to heal, if you're healthy.

PASSENGER

Then you went back to sea ?

STOKER

I went back to sea, and the next time it was a Dornier coming out of low cloud off the Humber. A bomb struck the after-end of the engine-room casing, another exploded alongside and started some plates. The sea came in quickly. But I was lucky that day. I was on deck when the bombs fell, and though a funnel-stay, parting like a fiddle-string, came down and broke my left arm, I got

into a boat. Into the only one that got away.
We were picked up and put ashore the next night.

PASSENGER

Then you went back to sea ?

STOKER

I was in hospital for some time. Then I came
back, or I wouldn't be here now.

PASSENGER

And why do you always go back to sea ?

SECOND MATE

What else should he do ? He is a sailor.

WIRELESS OPERATOR

And sailors do their duty. . . . I meant that for
a joke, but it isn't a very good one, is it ? For they
do. But don't ask me why. I suppose they have
a sense of duty, but God knows where it comes

from. It isn't that England has given them so rich rewards that all their hearts must overflow with gratitude. England has never given them more than a scavenger's wage, a dirty bunk in the bows of a six-thousand-ton tramp when afloat, and two rooms in a slum when ashore.

STOKER

My wife always kept them clean and tidy, and the child was well-dressed too.

WIRELESS OPERATOR

You may have had a wife who looked after you, but that doesn't mean you had a Government that looked after you. Once I read, in some book I found, that men must be taught to serve the good, the beautiful, and the true. But has England ever taught you even to recognise either goodness or truth ? Where, in your life, have you known beauty ?

STOKER

Sometimes at sea. And at home.

7

The Raft

Even in time of peace the sea has peril enough, of hurricane, iceberg, and fog, uncharted wreck and treacherous reef. But in time of war there is danger unceasing. A ship is only a skin of iron that encloses a dead weight of cargo, great engines, and a handful or a small town-ful of men. Break open the skin — it is tender, the warhead of a torpedo will open a cathedral door in it — and all those men are adrift on the huge enmity of the sea. They crowd into a little boat, or a thing of matchwood like this, and the nearest land, it may be, is twelve hundred miles away.

Now, in the deadliest time of the war, Germany is sinking week after week two hundred thousand tons of our shipping. More than that. The seas are strewn with wreckage. Under every quarter of the sky there are drifting little boats with quiet figures in them of sailors dead or dying. But the sailors who are rescued go back to sea. They do their duty. They go back, unflinching, to the fearful duty which no one has ever taught them.

LIEUTENANT

The heart of man is a boundless thing, and his
mind is a great instrument that will do marvels
if virtue move him. And virtue goes to sea in all
our ships, the virtue of our land, of the islands
that have left their fingerprint, for good or evil,
in every corner of the world. Chiefly for good,
is my belief. I believe in the people of this king-
dom. There is in their hearts an ancient thing,
native to their land, that has not of late been much
regarded, but is strong though it has no speech,
and is capable of greater deeds than have yet been
done. This I believe when I think of the sailors
who go back to sea.

PASSENGER

Such a faith has not been — shall we say,
obvious ? — in the young men of your generation.

LIEUTENANT

We were not living, till lately, in an age of
faith. It was an age of doubt. We used a passion-

ate scrutiny — my generation — and weighed in a goldsmith's balance all debatable values. We examined motives with a cold and suspecting eye, we were nervously aware of our faults, and we desired, without knowing how, to make better much that had been taken for good in the past. All that was a sign of life. It was a good generation, I think, but I agree with you when you say it had little faith. Faith began to come when we were put to the proof.

PASSENGER

There were those, of your generation, who did much harm by making of their intellect a barrier between themselves and their fellow-men. They appeared to believe that intellectuals need have no contact with the common herd, and could find no pleasure in its way of life. Surely intellect should be a general servant? But they made of it a private plaything.

LIEUTENANT

Wasn't it the common herd which drove the poor intellectuals into a sort of reservation, as though we were the surviving members of a Red

Indian tribe in Arizona? The great majority, having decided that thinking made them uncomfortable, took pleasure in activities which prevented them from thinking. They felt guilty, however, and in the presence of people who still found it agreeable to exercise intelligence they were ill-at-ease, and showed it. The little company of intellectuals, being as sensitive as the others, thereupon withdrew to their reservation.

PASSENGER

You might, I think, have made of your intelligence a more persuasive thing. Despite an air of confidence, the English are in some ways a diffident people. They are not easily upset by war and discomfort, but they are mortally afraid of ideas. And you intellectuals, dealing in brand-new ideas, dealt with them in so truculent a fashion that you frightened us out of our wits. You compelled us to seek comfort in the simpler noises of creation, such as the yelping of greyhounds, or the dance-orchestras that made such a very similar noise. Yes, you frightened us.

GUNNER

There was a friend of mine who used to be very easily alarmed by any loud noise.

PASSENGER

That isn't exactly what I meant. . . . But tell me about your friend.

GUNNER

He has been killed in the war. I have been thinking about him a great deal during these last few days.

LIEUTENANT

Where do you come from, Gunner?

GUNNER

From Stornoway. That is in the island of Lewis, which you will have heard about.

PASSENGER

Was your friend a sailor?

GUNNER

No, he was in the Cameron Highlanders. He was my cousin as well as being my friend, and he joined the Camerons nearly six years ago, because that was the regiment that his father, my uncle, used to be in. My cousin was killed on the mountains that rise in front of Keren. It was a long battle there, and Andrew, my cousin, was afraid nearly all the time.

SECOND MATE

Keren? In Eritrea? They'd have gone ashore at Port Sudan, where the sun hits you like the blow of a hammer. I was there in a troopship, that was in the winter of 1940, but we were carrying Indian soldiers. I didn't see any Camerons.

GUNNER

The Indian soldiers were also very good. But I will tell you about Andrew.

There were two subalterns who led his Company to the attack. They had three hours' climbing from the valley to the ridge, over naked rock where the only cover was a little thorn-scrub, and all the way they were under fire. The sun was hot upon their backs, but the sweat ran down their arms, and when the bullets came it was like the little draughts of cold air you will sometimes feel on your neck. The Italians were strong there. They held the mountain-tops with many guns, they had guns in the crannies and caves of the rocks, and nine men out of ten, looking at those heights, would have said, ' They can never be taken.'

But the Camerons, a Company led by two subalterns not long out of school, went up the nearest ridge. They made use of the ground in a clever way, like stalkers, and as well as being clever, their blood was up. So they took a corner of the ridge, and held it till morning. Then the rest of the Battalion came up, under fire from a mountain called Dologorodoc, over the gorge, and they held the ridge against all attack for thirteen days.

That was the crest that was given the name of Cameron Ridge. Beyond it there was a wilder range, with a big rough head on it called Sanchil. It was attacked by English soldiers and by Indians, who were as brave as any story of bravery in the world. But they could not take it. So the Camerons on Cameron Ridge lay under fire from the heights beyond. They were blistered and flayed by the midday sun, but in the bitter winds at night their teeth would be chattering and their fingers white with cold.

There was no water on the ridge. Every pint of water and every bandolier of ammunition had to be carried, by the men themselves, over the rocks from the valley below.

So the battle went on. The Camerons were relieved by the Fusiliers, then they returned and made an attack on Sanchil. It was not easy. They had to go through a barrage of mortar-bombs, climbing that steep rock, and the machine-gun fire was like a hailstorm in the cliffs. But then you saw, coming through the storm with their heads up, little groups of men. Six men — there was a young officer, a quartermaster, and a cook among them — were all that was left of one Company. There were seventeen out of another Company, and about a dozen from two Companies that had started together. They gathered near the top of Sanchil, as if it were under the forehead of the mountain. They held a crevice here, a cranny there, and all the rock was as hot as a frying-pan under the sun. Then they attacked the very crown of the rock. But there were too few of them and the Italians beat them back, throwing little bombs that burst at their feet.

But about ten days later the West Yorks took the mountain called Dologorodoc, over the gorge, and then it was easy to capture Sanchil. And our men, who went there, found on the very top of Sanchil the bodies of three Cameron Highlanders. It was a good Battalion.

LIEUTENANT

That, I think, is what one calls an understatement.

PASSENGER

But how do you know all this?

GUNNER

I saw it. No, I was not there. I was at sea. But I saw it all very clearly because of what happened to my cousin Andrew.

PASSENGER

What did happen?

GUNNER

He was in the battle till the last day. But all the time the noise of the guns put such fear into him that his body was trembling, and his jaw loosened and shook like a broken shutter in the wind. He could not grow used to the noise, like the other men, who were indifferent when the sky seemed to gather its breath and cough like thunder under the cliffs.

There was an officer who knew Andrew, and was sorry for him. He said that Andrew must be ill, and told him to go and see the doctor. So presently, in a quiet hour, Andrew went down the hill. But very soon he returned and told a story about some medicine the doctor had given him, that would be good for his fear and keep his jaw still when the guns opened fire.

He went back to his duty, to a rifleman's post in a cleft of the rock. And very soon the guns of the enemy let fly a salvo. The air was full of screaming, then the shells burst and the echo of the din of them was repeated four or five times, and Andrew's jaw hung loose with his fear and shook like a bill-board caught in the wind. But he lay by his rifle and made no move to escape.

He had never gone near the doctor. He knew that no doctor could cure him, and he would not waste the man's time. He just made up his mind that he would endure his fear, and not put the Battalion to shame. So he stayed on Cameron Ridge all those days, and suffered the agony of fear that loosened and shook his jaw like something adrift in a gale. — Even when he was a little boy he had never liked hearing a loud noise. — But fear never got the better of him. He did nothing that would make the Cameron Highlanders ashamed of him. He went forward in their last attack, and he was killed under the forehead of Sanchil. There were some good men in that Battalion.

PASSENGER

If there were any better than your cousin Andrew, they were truly remarkable.

18

GUNNER

He was a quiet, well-spoken fellow, and I was very fond of him.

LIEUTENANT

But why — this is the question — why did he make that resolution to endure his fear ?

SECOND MATE

I don't see any mystery there. He was a soldier in a good regiment, and he had to behave like a soldier.

LIEUTENANT

That is the answer you gave when I asked why sailors, whose ships had been torpedoed, went back to face the danger of the sea. ' Because they were sailors,' you said. But think what has lately been happening in Britain. When the cities were bombed — London, Coventry, Manchester, Bristol, Hull, and many others — the men and women of those cities also went back to work. Green-

grocers and carpenters and clerks and charwomen :
they went back to work. And why ? You would
answer, I suppose, 'Because they *were* greengrocers. Because they *were* carpenters and clerks
and charwomen.'

SECOND MATE

What else could they do but go back to work ?

LIEUTENANT

At other times, and in other countries, people
have submitted to fear. They have been defeated.

SECOND MATE

Did you expect us to throw up the sponge at
the first blow ?

STOKER

From the way some people talked, in the years
before the war, you might have expected that very
thing to happen. I have heard it said, at street-
corners in our own country, and in many seaport
towns abroad, that Britain was old and worn-out,
and fit for nothing good.

The Raft

PASSENGER

Many nations, and most people, I think, go to some trouble to hide their faults and dissemble their vices. We in these islands of Britain had recently the singular habit of concealing our virtue. The fashionable shade of an English complexion, for a generation or so, was lack-lustre.

LIEUTENANT

And now we have been compelled, reluctantly I suppose, to reveal the virtue within us. Britain, so far from being worn-out and fit for nothing good, is crowded-full of soldiers and sailors, of clerks, carpenters, charwomen, and greengrocers who insist on doing their duty in face of the enemy. But no one will tell me why.

PASSENGER

Will you not tell us?

LIEUTENANT

Have you ever been to Westminster Abbey?

PASSENGER

Occasionally.

STOKER

I've seen it from the outside. I've never been in.

WIRELESS OPERATOR

You can't see much there nowadays. Half of it is full of sandbags.

LIEUTENANT

The nave of Westminster Abbey is two feet higher than the nave of York Minster, which is a hundred feet high. I once read that in a guide-book, and as I read it I saw the great army of English builders, in the years of faith, raising yet higher and higher their lovely roofs and great towers against the English sky. Count in your memory the number of the English cathedrals: Canterbury and York, Salisbury and Westminster and Wells, Durham and Ely — how many are there ? There was a time when England gave more enthusiasm to the building of churches than we have ever given to the building of an empire. And don't they seem, the greatest of the churches, to be competing the one against the other ? Why were they built so tall and splendid ?

PASSENGER

A sense of religious duty must have been the fundamental reason, but equally, I think, there was pleasure in the art of building. And the cathedrals are also an expression of pride.

LIEUTENANT

A sense of duty, and pride. That's what built them. And that is what takes your sailors back to sea, and soldiers into battle, and greengrocers and charwomen to their work when their work is dangerous. Duty to the cause for which they fight or work, and pride in what they are. I believe in the people of these islands : not only in their goodness, but their sufficient strength. And to say this, now at this time, is an act of faith. The war has still to be won, and when the war has been won, there is peace to be made. Much of our strength has been broken in battle, and we take no delight in the war. But Britain is stronger than ever before, and pledged to endure. The people will endure. But when the war is over, they must take up another burden. Much of the world will have to be built anew, and better built than before. Britain must take her share, and not a small one, in that building. She will need all her sense of duty, and she will need her pride.

PASSENGER

Then she must bring it into the open. If pride is to be of proper service, it must be conscious. But we, for a long time now, have stifled our pride. Stifled it so effectively that its voice has gone. It has forgotten how to speak. It whispers in our secret heart, but that is not enough.

LIEUTENANT

No, it is not enough. Pride must come out of the dark.

WIRELESS OPERATOR

You're asking too much of Britain if you expect her to carry the world on her back. There'll be work enough, for all our people, in putting our own country to rights, after the war. If they manage to do that, they'll have done plenty.

LIEUTENANT

I should like to see much of Britain built again — suburb and factory, schools and railway stations and city streets — in the delight of building, with the pride and beauty, that moved the years when the cathedrals were built.

WIRELESS OPERATOR

Then why bother about foreign countries? Why shouldn't we give all our energy, and all our time, to making a really good job of our own?

SECOND MATE

Because we can't afford to be selfish. You can put it, if you like, that the world sails in convoy nowadays, and the well-being of one nation is bound to another. I have spent my life in ships, and ships don't go to sea for the amusement of their owners and the health of their crews. They go for trade. But if we don't look after our customers there'll be no foreign trade, and our last voyage will be to Carey Street.

WIRELESS OPERATOR

We have meddled too much with foreign countries. This is what Britain did : it woke up early, while other people were still asleep, and went out and grabbed an empire. And now, whenever we talk of freedom, our breath stinks of all the places we've killed and robbed.

LIEUTENANT

It is so much easier to blame than to praise. Until I grew up I could see very little good in the British Empire, but slowly, as I learnt something about the world as it is, I began to think better of it. Does it really make a bad smell in the world ? Is it nothing but the creation of a dead hand ? Consider one of the smallest of our colonies :

Malta. Would Malta have made for itself a new name of gallantry if we, the imperial power, had crushed the life and spirit of its people? If you summon Britain to court on a charge of imperialism, is Malta not a witness for the defence?

GUNNER

If Malta gave evidence, it would sound very like the story of David and Goliath. The Philistines, you will remember, stood on a mountain, and Israel stood on a mountain on the other side, and there was a valley between them. And a champion came out of the camp of the Philistines, whose name was Goliath of Gath. He was wearing a helmet of brass and a coat of mail that weighed five thousand shekels of brass, and he had a shield of brass, and brass upon his legs. His spear was as thick as a weaver's beam, and the head of it weighed six hundred shekels of iron. But when David went against him, David was wearing no more than a boy would be wearing.

Nevertheless David said, 'Let no man's heart fail because of him. Thy servant will go and fight with this Philistine.'

So David took five smooth stones out of a brook, and put them in a kind of a bag, and his sling was in his hand. And when Goliath came within range he put a hand in his bag and took out a stone, and slung it. And he smote Goliath in his forehead, so that the stone sunk into his forehead, and Goliath fell upon his face to the earth.

LIEUTENANT

So the air-fleets of Rome and Germany, heavily armed, brassily arrogant, made war against Malta. But Malta, like young David, pelted them shrewdly, and their bombers came tumbling down. ' Let no man's heart fail because of them,' said Malta. ' Thy servant will fight with these Philistines.'

PASSENGER

It is a good argument. Malta, for one, has not been frozen by the dead hand of imperialism.

LIEUTENANT

And the great Dominions that we planted do not look like dead growths. Have you ever seen the fathom-high soldiers of Australia, leather-skinned, swaggering, talking as though they had never breathed anything less than a gale snatched out of the sky, their boots striking the ground as if earth were a ball for their play?

Do you know the great width of Canada, the silver-streaked mountains, the prairie-gold ocean of wheat, the lakes in the wind and the cloud-soaring cities? In the fall of the year the estuary of the St. Lawrence is most beautiful. It is lined with a crimson forest. And it would need, I think, a mouth as wide as the St. Lawrence to tell the whole story of Canada's delight in being Canada.

Remember, too, the armies that fought, a year or so back, from the highlands of Kenya through fever-swamp, thorn-scrub and desert, over the Juba river, and took at a swoop the town like a sneeze, Mogadisciu, then leapt with a roar that frightened the Tuscans high into Ogaden, so to the mountains of blasted stone, and over them, still at a run, to Harar, Jijiga, and down the new Roman road to Haile Selassie's drab capital city. That campaign over — the swiftest that ever was won — they stooped like an eagle, out of the African sky, on the enemy lines on the Cyrenaican border, and fought with high spirit and speed and the toughest resolve in that sour debatable land. They were South Africans, most of that army. Forty years ago they were fighting against us. But between us we made up a peace that not only stitched but healed the wounds of that war. And now in this war for To-morrow, this battle that's joined on the cross-roads of Time, we are fighting together.

For some little time the sound of unsynchronised engines has been heard, growing steadily louder, and now dominating the continuous soft noises of the sea.

WIRELESS OPERATOR

Do you hear that? It's an aeroplane.

PASSENGER

It has come too late.

SECOND MATE

Yes, too late to help us — if it is one of ours.

STOKER

And if it is one of theirs, well, it's too late to do us any harm.

The noise grows louder, rises to a scream and abruptly fades, as the aeroplane dives low upon the raft and rises beyond it.

LIEUTENANT

If it is one of ours they will go home and say : 'We found six dead men on a raft.' But if they could see the truth, they would say : 'We found six men with a living faith.'

PASSENGER

I am older than you, and faith is more difficult for me. But in this matter that divides the world we have right on our side, we have not wasted our strength in fighting for it, and good will come of the fight. Our country is a tree that bears good fruit. That I believe. That is the message I would give them.

WIRELESS OPERATOR

I don't know if I believe or not, but I have played for my side.

STOKER

I would give them a message to my wife. . . .

The noise returns, swelling to a roar. The aeroplane dives again. Machine-guns open fire. The bullets tear white flakes from the sodden wood of the raft, and make fountains in the sea. But no one is hit. The stammer of gunfire ceases, the engine-noise grows less and dies away.

PASSENGER

I found that very comforting. I was, and still am, a peace-loving man. Though I saw from the beginning the necessity of this war, I could not for a long time play a part in it with any enthusiasm. Because even a good war is a very beastly thing. How comforting, then, to see a last glimpse of the enemy.

GUNNER

They used to come down and shoot at fishermen in their open boats. It was not a generous thing to do.

LIEUTENANT

That is their ultimate condemnation: they have no generosity. And no one should set out to conquer even a village, let alone the world, if he is not generous.

WIRELESS OPERATOR

I don't admire them for shooting at fishermen in open boats, or at dead men on a raft, but have we the right to condemn them? I read a book about the Indian Mutiny, not the sort of book you read in school, but an honest book, and according to it we behaved then almost as badly as the Germans.

PASSENGER

At the time of the Mutiny there were only a few thousand Englishmen in India. When the sepoys rose against them, they were very naturally afraid. And being frightened they did certain things which were unforgivable, but not incomprehensible. You cannot, however, say that our policy in India has been one of constant brutality and suppression.

WIRELESS OPERATOR

A lot of Indians do say that, and say it openly.

PASSENGER

Then the policy of suppression cannot be very rigorously applied.

SECOND MATE

I've been in India. In Bombay, and Calcutta, and Madras, and a dozen other places. I've seen their local newspapers, and till you've read what Indian papers are allowed to write about the British administration, you don't know what freedom of speech really means. Don't talk about suppression to me.

The Raft

A lot of nonsense has been written about India, by people who know nothing of the land and little of its history. They call it a nation nowadays, and say therefore it has the right to determine its own future. But who made it a nation?

There was a king called Asoka, two hundred years before Christ, and he, perhaps, unified it then. But two hundred years before Gandhi there was chaos, and a parcel of adventurers—courtiers of the dead Moguls and wiry Maratha generals — were carving, like bandits at a feast, the body of Hindustan into gobbets of meat. For long ages India had been shredded by conquest, then patched up to pay revenue, and shredded again. The nation vanished, and no memory of it remained.

SECOND MATE

There was a story I heard about one of the invaders of India called Sultan Mahmud of Ghazni. He came down from the north, and conquered Gujerat, on the west coast. There was a very holy temple at a place called Somnath, and the Hindus did their best to keep him out of that, because the most famous idol of their god Siva stood in the shrine. But Mahmud forced his way in, and struck the idol with his club. It broke open, and a stream of jewels ran out.

PASSENGER

That is the story of Mahmud of Ghazni, and for a long time it was the story of all India. There was a recipe for wealth : Strike India. We also, in the beginning, struck India. We went in, and shook the pagoda-tree.

But that is not the whole story. We imposed our peace, and gave India the rule of law. If now it claims to be a nation, it is because we have given it that peace which is the mother of thought and womb of consciousness. Many upright men of our race have served India with all their strength. With honesty and perseverance. They gave their service for love of the land and its people, out of a steadfast belief in the justice they taught and imposed. No one denies that we first went into India for the reason that took Mahmud of Ghazni there ; but the sons of the first traders went back as the servants of India, and the children of those who plundered returned to teach, and the conquering soldiers remained on guard. Look at the balance now. Lay on the one side the tattered lands that were left when the Moguls died; on the other scale set the nation that clamours to-day, not for mercy, but equal place with our own.—Have we repaid?

SECOND MATE

I say we have done well by India.

LIEUTENANT

Conquerors do not usually teach their subjects that men have the right, and nations the right, to be free. But that has been our lesson. We have built an empire, but not of slaves. We have taught and maintained the law that the weak and the strong have equal rights under law, and now India brings us into court in the name of our law. Surely that means we have been good teachers?

PASSENGER

Empire-building is a foolish and misleading

phrase. It calls to mind the building of pyramids, great monuments of power built of dead stone. What we have done has been more like creation, and India, loudly articulate and full of argument, is proof that our rule doesn't destroy, but gives life.

LIEUTENANT

I was speaking of the four Dominions when the aeroplane came to show us the meaning of German rule. I had spoken of three. The soldiers of the fourth Dominion, New Zealand, I saw when I was serving aboard a destroyer in the Mediterranean. We took the remnant of them out of Greece after they had fought in that most heart-breaking of all campaigns. They were solid men, loving their native farms and the mountains of their own land. Then fortune took them to famous ground. They held, a single brigade of them, Leonidas' pass at Thermopylae. The Germans launched their attack with two armoured divisions and two mountain divisions. Their Stukas came screaming, bombed the coverless roads. For eleven days the attack rolled up to the pass, and beaten, fell back. Like the long-haired Spartans before them, the men from New Zealand held fast. Stalwart men, stock of these islands, and Maoris. A single brigade, they defended Thermopylae. You cannot say that New Zealand has come to its manhood with a spirit poorly nourished.

PASSENGER

A good gardener, they say, has green fingers. What he plants will grow. And it seems to me that Britain has also had green fingers. We have been conquerors, I know, but only at intervals and often in a very casual and unpremeditated way. It is more important to remember that we have been good gardeners.

WIRELESS OPERATOR

Do you think we have been good gardeners in our own country? Do you remember unemployment before the war, and the semi-starvation that went with it? Have you ever seen the slums in our seaport towns? Do you think that all the millions we have spent on so-called education have been well spent? Have you ever heard of depressed areas in Durham and South Wales?

STOKER

Yes, and in the Highlands of Scotland too. I have a brother who was a minister in Portree, before he went into the Army, and he has told me that in the first forty years of last century the island of Skye sent nearly eleven thousand men into the British Army, and twenty-one Generals and a Governor-General of India too. That was from Skye alone, but the total number from all the islands and the Highlands was very large indeed. We cannot find so great a number to-day, because the Highlands have been very much neglected. And that is a pity.

LIEUTENANT

Nobody is going to deny that we have made tragic mistakes and committed the most destructive follies. Nobody, I hope, will ever suggest that we should keep silent about our faults and national misdeeds and acts of lunacy. But it would be ridiculous to talk about nothing else. In justice to ourselves we should speak, from time to time, of what we have done well. Are we not entitled, now and then, to remember with pleasure those matters in which we have been successful? Would it be wholly unforgivable if, on occasion, we were even to congratulate ourselves on some of the wise and timely actions we have taken?

PASSENGER

Hammer that nail home. We have dispraised and underrated ourselves too long.

LIEUTENANT

We have certainly underrated ourselves. You know the way in which people nowadays regard the pilots and air-crews of the Royal Air Force? As if they were a race apart, men with some incomprehensible virtue and mysterious superhuman qualities. But a year or two ago those pilots and navigators and air-gunners were the people we rubbed shoulders with in the streets. We took no particular notice of them then. They were clerks and mechanics, they were accountants and shopmen, they were sheep-farmers, they sold second-hand motor-cars and life-insurance and radio sets, they were agents and managers and ironmongers and bus-conductors.

PASSENGER

They were even the products of those public schools which have been the object of so much unkind criticism.

LIEUTENANT

They were the ordinary people of our country. But in those ordinary people was a virtue, a strength, a mystery that we did not recognise. We underrated them. And we know, now, that we underrated the whole country.

WIRELESS OPERATOR

We may have underrated its potentialities, but for a good long time it would have been very difficult to underrate its performance.

SECOND MATE

Let's not start a post-mortem on Britain-before-the-war. I've got a feeling it would make me slightly uncomfortable, being not more than a couple of cables from post-mortem myself.

PASSENGER

We suffer, as a nation, from lack of imagination. That has often been a comfort, but more often a handicap. Lack of imagination — of imaginative perception — kept us from seeing fighter-pilots and navigators in those ordinary young men whom we used to meet in suburban trains and city offices. Yet we all know the strands in our history : the English admirals and the English poets, yeomen farmers and strong craftsmen, the same stock in the foundries to-day who tempered swords for Agincourt and made cannon for Francis Drake. We should have been confident enough, but we doubted everything. Then came the year when we stood alone, when France had fallen, all Europe was captive, when Russia held its fire and America was not yet ready. Then at last, when we had no visible reason for confidence, confidence returned. Standing alone at the cross-roads, unarmed and naked, we discovered a little fragment of the truth : we knew, at least, that we should never give in.

The Raft

No one shared that knowledge. All the world believed that we had been defeated. It took me a long time to understand how deeply that belief was held. I have been in America for nearly three months. My ship went there for repairs, and we lay in the Philadelphia Navy Yard for six weeks, and then I fell ill and had to stay behind when she sailed. My American friends were more kind and generous than I could have believed possible, but they shocked me when they confessed their belief that after Dunkirk we were beaten.

PASSENGER

I have been in America longer than you. They had no choice but to suppose we were beaten, because all that preserved us from defeat was something that lay so deep in our hearts, so secret and long-neglected, that we ourselves had more than half forgotten its existence. We gave them no encouragement to believe in us. They had to find the secret for themselves, and this is the story I was told.

44

For a long time the information which the President had been receiving was all of the most dismal kind. He was told about the weakness of Britain, the sinking of our ships, our failure to re-arm with proper speed. About political quarrelling and the enmity between capital and labour. About our slackness, our stupidity, our cynicism. All the bad things and every circumstance that promised our defeat were carried to his ears. But the President, in spite of all the evidence, was not wholly convinced. He, perhaps, knew more about us than we did ourselves. He has never lacked — what did I call it ? — imaginative perception.

So he sent to Britain a special emissary, a friend of his, a man in whose judgment he trusted. And this man went to and fro about Britain, in the winter when London was burning, and spoke to the people. Not only to Cabinet Ministers and great industrialists. He spoke to them, of course, and to Admirals and senior Civil Servants. But he spent most of his time with quite humble people, in factories and shipyards and football grounds, in narrow streets, in tram-cars and the corner pub. He learned for himself the true temper of Britain. But for a time he said nothing. He would not disclose what opinion he had formed, and no one knew whether it was good or ill.

Then, after he had been here for some weeks, he was invited to a dinner-party in Scotland. There were about a dozen people there, all of them important. The Prime Minister was there. After dinner the Prime Minister made a little speech, and so did one or two others. Then the American, the President's emissary, got up to speak. He had spent the day, after his usual manner, among ordinary people. He spoke of this and that, but said nothing of any consequence. Then he paused for a little while, and continued in this way :

' It occurs to me that some of you may be interested to know what impression I have formed, of your country and its people, during the short time I have been here. You are aware, I suppose, that the attitude of the United States of America may to some extent be influenced by what I have to say about you. And to the best of my knowledge you are inclined to attach some importance to America's attitude. You would not regard with indifference, let us say, the prospect of whole-hearted American assistance in this war you are waging. Well, gentlemen, what I have learnt about your country and your people, from your people, has now made me bold enough to anticipate the verdict of my country. Speaking in the name of my country, and the words of the Bible, I say to you : " Whither thou goest, I will go ; thy people shall be my people, and thy God my God." '

LIEUTENANT

That evening, whenever it was, anticipated history. Everybody there, hearing that promise, must have known that victory, however long it might take to come, had been assured.

SECOND MATE

And what assured it was the ordinary people of Great Britain. They were the evidence. Your American emissary found his proof in the pubs and the buses, in the factories and the streets. It was the people who convinced him.

LIEUTENANT

I believe in their virtue and their strength, in the kindliness and good-humour of their hearts, in the justice of their intention.

WIRELESS OPERATOR

I believe in freedom and fair play for all. I believe that England might have done better than she has — but she might have done worse.

GUNNER

I believe in Scotland, though she is like an old bitch that has suckled too many puppies, and her whelps have gone far from her. But there is no beauty like the beauty of her mountains and the islands and the sea-lochs on a summer evening. And the Highland regiments have fought very well in this war.

LIEUTENANT

I believe in the Royal Navy, that has been stretched over all the seas of the world, and has fought the most desperate of all its wars.

PASSENGER

I believe that in the mystery of life there is benignity. I believe that in the mystery of these islands there is a weapon capable of serving that benignity.

LIEUTENANT

Read the whole story of Britain. Weigh on the one side all we have given, weigh on the other what we have taken. We have given more. It is a good story, though some of the chapters read darkly, and this also I believe, that the story is only beginning. There are new victories we shall win, new territories we shall explore. We shall march against the oldest enemies, against fear and cruelty, untruth and greed. We shall send our voyagers into the new lands of peace and justice, of understanding and high endeavour. When this war against Germany is over, the soldiers and the sailors will go back to their homes, but faith and duty and pride must not lay down their weapons. The faith and duty we have found in these years may not disarm, nor sober pride return to sleep. They will be needed still, for them there is no discharge. Keep them in service, and we shall do great things. We are still in the early days of our story.—All this I believe.

STOKER

I believe in my wife and child. She is a good woman, honest and laughing and kind, and the child is well cared-for. I believe, or I used to believe, in my own strength and the mates I've had in the stoke-hole of a dozen ships. I believe in the people in our street. They were good to us when I was out of work.—But what's the point of all this ? We are what we are, and if there was no good in us we'd have rotted and gone long since. You needn't look for perfection, now nor ever, and there are rats in every ship. Too many rats. But the rats don't rule the ship. Don't worry too much about the rats. Take the toe of your boot to them, and go to work. Give us work to do, and we're all right. Give us good work, and we'll do it well. Yes, give us good ships, and put them to good use, and we'll take them to sea. Set us a proper course, and we shan't fail you.

LIEUTENANT

Set us a proper course. . . .

There is silence, but for the chop of broken water on the raft, the lapsing of the sea, and the wind combing the tops of the swell. The slap of a wave, a sound like that of a pebble dropped into a deep well, the whistle of wind in the trough : nothing else.

Then a steamer's whistle is heard, and repeated. Presently there is the urgent noise that a boat makes in a heavy sea : the forefoot thudding on a wave, spray falling thickly, splash of oars. Then voices are heard.

FIRST VOICE

Easy, starboard. Easy ! Give way, port. . . . Look alive, now. Steady there. Get aboard and make fast to something.

SECOND VOICE

Aye, aye, sir.

51

THIRD VOICE

If it hadn't been for that Dornier diving and shooting at them, we'd never have seen them.

FOURTH VOICE

We're too late, anyway. They're all dead, aren't they ?

FIRST VOICE

All right forward ? What do they look like ? Any alive ?

SECOND VOICE

I can't make out, sir.

FIRST VOICE

I'll come and have a look.—Get that oar out of the way ! You're a sailor now, not a billiard-marker.

FOURTH VOICE

They're all dead, sir.

The Raft

FIRST VOICE

What do you know about it?—Here's one that's
alive. And another.—Come on, now, get moving!
Cut that line away. Cut it, you beetle-fingered
gravedigger! Come on, billiard-marker, take a
hold of this fellow. Easy now. Careful with his
head.

FOURTH VOICE

Are they still alive?

FIRST VOICE

Alive? Of course they're alive. Men like
these don't die as easy as you'd think.

SOCRATES ASKS WHY

A Second Conversation in Elysium

The scene is the loggia of a country club in Elysium. Though the architecture is Palladian, the furniture betrays a modern taste for comfort, and upholstery has not all been sacrificed to design. A bank of azaleas, growing beneath a low balustrade, is almost luminous in the ebb of day.

The time is also hinted by the demeanour of those present, who wear the easy look of men who have dined. SOCRATES, *indeed, is yawning, and another is asleep.* SOCRATES *is a shortish thick-set man, bearded, with a big mouth, eyes like a bull, a snub nose with great nostrils. His woollen himation, carelessly worn, is not quite clean.*

In neighbouring chairs — they are not purposely in one party, but near enough for conversation — are ABRAHAM LINCOLN, M. DE VOLTAIRE, *and* DR. JOHNSON.

LINCOLN'S *appearance in Elysium has already been*

described in The Cornerstones. JOHNSON, *a vast and sprawling figure, resembles the portrait by Reynolds rather than Macaulay's description; though his coat is inelegant, it bears little evidence of his liking for fish sauce, and the rugged magnificence of his face wears no unseemly scars. But his speech is still explosive with puffing and grunting, and his gestures reveal rather the energy of his mind than the perfection of his manners.* VOLTAIRE, *thickly gowned even against the mild air of an Elysian evening, is a pair of eyes, a long thin nose, and a grin below a powdered wig.*

The sleeper reclines at the other end of the loggia. He is dressed, more formally than the others, in black. His brow is a bony cliff. His cheek-bones, from which the sleeping flesh has receded, are broad and harsh. His mouth, like that of a swimming giant come up for breath, gapes wide open. His hands, folded on his chest, are twitching. It is BEETHOVEN.

Conveniently placed for the entertainment of the others is one of those Elysian television-sets which, with their unrestricted range and free selection, allow the inhabitants to see all they want of the world's activity. At the moment an official Commentator, in a rich professional voice, is describing the progress of the war; and on the screen there is a picture of desperate fighting on the green hills of the Bataan Peninsula. But the view changes abruptly to a glimpse of oil-derricks and the aspiring, many-windowed rectangles of a sunlit American city.

COMMENTATOR

The Bataan Peninsula was defended by its weary garrison of American and Filipino soldiers with such dauntless fury that it seemed the whole crop of human bravery and tenacity had been gathered for their hearts alone. The Japanese had to pay a fearful price for victory. Their enormous strength was hugely mutilated, but the attack was unceasing, and the concentrated multitude of men and guns was finally irresistible. But America was not slow to respond, and now, in the cities of the United States, we can see the prodigious evidence of her determination to match a world in arms. The mind trembles at the brutal enormity of the war, for upon its issue depends the whole future of the world. But America meets the challenge ! America is working, drilling, casting cannon, and building ships. America is spending money that reaches into figures which hitherto only astronomers have employed. Mr. Roosevelt has asked for an appropriation of $10,000,000,000 for naval expansion. . . .

LINCOLN, *after a questioning glance to the others and their assenting gesture, turns off both Voice and View.*

LINCOLN

Either the world has got braver since my time, or is become insensitive. I remember getting a letter from Horace Greeley, just after the first battle of Bull Run. In New York, he said, ' sullen, scorching, black despair sits on every brow.' Yet this war, so immeasurably vaster than ours, and beginning as it did with surprise and disaster, has not induced despair, but high spirits and determination. I would very much like to know what Horace thinks about this amendment to our spiritual constitution. He would approve, I know, of Mr. Roosevelt's financial policy, for Horace had a lavish way with money himself.

VOLTAIRE

I begin to feel doubtful about the impartiality of our Commentator. I incline more and more to the belief that it was he who instigated this doleful war. There is in his voice a deepening note of gratification when he tells us how big it is. He reminds me of a theatrical producer who has put upon the stage the most extravagant spectacle of all time, and hopes by advertising its enormous cost to excuse its lack of taste.

LINCOLN

But surely he is justified in combing the dictionary for every superlative he can find. If we are to realise even a fraction of this war's significance, we must strain our minds to the very limit of comprehension. There is nothing in human speech that can exaggerate its size, or overestimate its consequences. If we exclude the story of the Flood — and as no one here has ever seen Noah, I think we may — then this certainly is the most general calamity in history. No war has ever counted (God help them all) so many participants.

JOHNSON

You are wrong, sir. The perpetual conflict

between Passion and Reason, extending over the whole terrestrial surface of the globe, engages all mankind.

LINCOLN

But there is sometimes a truce in that campaign.

VOLTAIRE

Nor has it the energy of total war, for while our sympathy, of course, is all enlisted upon the one side, our behaviour often takes service with the other. And so there is some dispersal of our forces.

JOHNSON

So much the worse for us.

LINCOLN

In the American Civil War nearly a million men lost their lives. It was a war for a good cause, it was a right and necessary war. But even now I cannot think without dismay of what it cost, and in the Southern States it left a heritage of poverty and bitterness that lasted all the years of a lifetime. And that war was confined to a single country. Do you dare to picture the casualty lists in this war, that has no boundaries except the limits that God has so mercifully given to our world ? What fearful ghosts will remain of hatred and utter misery ! How many Germans and Russians have already died in the snow, and on the banks of those red rivers ? How many English boys have died in the desert, or in the greater desolation of the sea ? What myriads of Chinese have gone to their death ! How many of my countrymen will perish in lands to which they never gave a thought ? There must be, in this new chaos, twenty, thirty, forty million men in arms.

SOCRATES

Why ?

LINCOLN

You ask me why ?

SOCRATES

Yes. What are they fighting for ?

LINCOLN

My country was attacked by an unscrupulous enemy without warning, without provocation, without other reason than the lust of aggression. Is that a sufficient answer ?

SOCRATES

But America is also at war with Germany, and Germany has not bombed your cities or attacked your dependent islands. Why are you fighting Germany ?

LINCOLN

Because Germany and Japan are two nations tarred with the same brush. They are survivors of an older world. A brutal world of inequality and fear. That is why they are in alliance. They are the last of the slave-states. They're resurrectionists. They have dug up, from some old and haunted grave, those shapes of hideous cruelty and oppression that were, we thought, for ever buried. The rape of Nanking and the massacre of Lidice are evidence of their nature and the deliberate demonstration of their power. And their single policy, their avowed intention, is to increase that power till it covers the earth. If they could work their will, they would destroy not only men and cities, but all our way of life.

SOCRATES

America, then, is fighting to preserve its way of life ? That is to say, its manners, and morals, and philosophy. Are you satisfied that your American way of life is worth the sacrifice of a large number of its sturdiest and most energetic citizens ?

LINCOLN

It is a way of life that safeguards freedom of conscience, that has brought about good and friendly relations between the people of forty-eight States, and does what it can to promote their material welfare.

SOCRATES

There are, however, certain elements in your American way of life which are less desirable than freedom of conscience, and may not be worth so great a price?

LINCOLN

In every country on earth you will find elements which, so far from being worth the slightest effort to preserve them, inspire in all right-thinking men the desire to eliminate them.

SOCRATES

But those undesirable elements will, by a successful war, be preserved equally with the good elements of American civilisation. They may, indeed, even be encouraged to grow, because war loosens many of the moral bands which, in time of peace, we try to keep tied.

LINCOLN

That, unhappily, is very true.

SOCRATES

So that in going to war to preserve only what is good, you are no more certain of achieving your purpose than a gambler, rolling his dice, can be sure of throwing the number seven ?

LINCOLN

I think you underestimate, not only the better aspirations of American life, but our capacity for putting them in harness and making them work.

SOCRATES

Then I am glad you have corrected me, for I wanted to be assured of that. — Now as to Britain. Britain went to war in quite different circumstances. Britain was not attacked by Germany. If my memory is right, Britain went to war on behalf of Poland, though a year earlier it had refused to fight for Czechoslovakia. Surely, then, the reason for Britain's participation in the war was a particular and decisive admiration for the Polish way of life ?

VOLTAIRE

Which, in the general estimation of Britain, must have been superior to the Czechoslovak way of life.

SOCRATES

I agree with you. Now in what respect was Poland superior ?

JOHNSON

Sir, you are sophisticating. There was no such thing as an appraisal of the several claims to admiration, which may have been numerous, of the countries you denominate. The majority of Englishmen, though indifferent to neither when it was attacked, had until then been ignorant of both. The reason of our going to war was a simple one. It was to put a stop to an abuse which had become intolerable.

SOCRATES

And if some other nation, let us suppose France or Spain, were to acquire as great a strength as Germany's, and try to bend all other countries to its will, would you judge that also an abuse which had to be stopped by war ?

JOHNSON

Yes, sir. Both France and Spain, at one time

or another, were disposed to secure, by the subjugation of their neighbours' power, the vicious aggrandisement of their own. They went very far on their road to a domination of the world, till we put a spoke in the wheel.

VOLTAIRE

And if Britain tried, in a similar manner, to dominate the continent of Europe, would you agree that Britain should be stopped ?

JOHNSON

Why, sir, I confess that I might be tempted to judge my own country more leniently than some foreign adventurer. But I would expect France to resent the intrusion of England, and though I might not sympathise with your resentment, I would respect it.

SOCRATES

For a long time it was the declared policy of Britain to preserve in Europe what was known as the Balance of Power. Is not that, perhaps, the reason why Britain is now at war with Germany ?

JOHNSON

A balance, sir, is a very useful instrument. On the counter of a shop it guarantees honesty in trade, and in the hand of Justice it is the symbol of equity. Where the balance is equal, then neither side can bluster in the gross assurance of superior wealth, nor tremble for its precarious insufficiency. A balance, sir, is not to be despised, nor is he who adjusts it.

LINCOLN

I suppose you are aware, Doctor, of the view that is taken by my country of your Balance of Power. We do not regard it with much liking, certainly with no reverence, and nothing will persuade us to juggle with contributory weights.

JOHNSON

I am the more willing to listen to you, sir, because in my London days I would have shown too little agreement. I used to hate an American almost as deeply as I hated a Whig. But that, sir, may have been due to ignorance. Since my arrival here, I have changed my mind in several particulars. I have even lost something of my animosity to the Whig dogs, because one doesn't meet them here, and memory becomes more kind as absence grows longer. But in regard to America my conversion has been positive, and that is because no one who has enjoyed the benefit and pleasure of your company, Mr. President, could fail to think kindly of the country that nursed you.

LINCOLN

Lord Chesterfield himself couldn't be more graceful than that, Doctor, but I'm better pleased to hear it from you than I would be from him. And I hope you won't change your opinion if I continue to be sceptical about your diplomacy. I had a very interesting talk with a countryman of yours not so long ago, a young fellow called Arden, who was in your Royal Air Force before he got himself killed, and I gathered from him that the younger generation in Britain have no more respect for the Balance of Power than I have. What some of them want, according to Arden, is a rule of international law, guaranteed and to begin with enforced, by the leading members of the Allied nations : that is to say, Great Britain, Russia, China, and the United States.

SOCRATES

That, I grant you, would be an object or purpose corresponding in importance with the magnitude of the war. But is that fourfold rule of law the declared policy of the Allied nations ?

LINCOLN

No, I'm afraid it isn't. Not yet.

SOCRATES

It is, then, merely the aspiration of a few ?

LINCOLN

I believe that something of that kind is the aspiration of a great number of intelligent people.

SOCRATES

Who would not be satisfied with anything less ?

69

LINCOLN

They will certainly not be satisfied if, when the war shall be over, the world returns to that uneasy system of balancing power against power until both sides, overloaded with their horrible accumulation of guns and hatred and fear, upset the machine and bring to ruin a whole generation in its fall.

SOCRATES

It is a characteristic of man that he aspires to better things. It is, however, a characteristic of nature that most human aspirations come to nothing. And if this desire that the stability of law should replace the uncertain equipoise of nations is not, as you admit, the agreed and stated policy of the Allied Powers, but merely an expression of hope on the part of some well-meaning people who, for all I know, have little influence in the world, then it seems likely that their aspirations will succumb to nature, and fail. That being so, all this fighting is a waste, not only of time and effort, but also of soldiers' lives.

LINCOLN

Let us hope you are wrong.

SOCRATES

By all means let us hope so. But if, unhappily, I am right, then surely these millions of men now at war are fighting without a sufficient cause? Or have they some large and reasoned motive about which I am ignorant?

VOLTAIRE

Is it possible, Socrates, that after all these years the power of your mind is failing? Do you really believe that human beings are governed by reason?

SOCRATES

It is the faculty of reason which principally distinguishes man from the lower animals. When he renounces the government of reason, he must relapse into the anarchy of the beasts.

VOLTAIRE

Which is a circumstance as common in history as a shower of rain in London.

SOCRATES

Since my time there has been a great number of excellent teachers, of whom you, Voltaire, were not the least. Is it possible that a race of men which has heard so much wisdom should remember none of it ?

VOLTAIRE

The world is incapable of learning.

JOHNSON

That is not so, sir. The world is eminently susceptible to instruction, and the universal growth of knowledge is happily accompanied by a general increase of sensibility. It is true, sir, that progress or advancement in one particular is rarely seen without some decline or retrogradation in another. I dare say you have observed a man, hurrying to his place of business, who sets his foot upon a piece of orange-peel, and thereby takes a fall ? But will any good man be distracted from his vocation by such a trivial interruption ? No, sir, he will not. He will pick himself up and proceed as though nothing had happened.

VOLTAIRE

Do you really share the optimism of a certain creature of my fancy whom I called — if my memory is good — Dr. Pangloss ?

JOHNSON

No, sir. The world is not the best of all possible worlds, but it is a tolerable world, and a strong man should not despair of its growing better. It has grown better in many of its aspects. Twenty years ago I contemplated the Russian revolution with every degree of antipathy and revulsion, but I am bound to admit that the Russian army of to-day is a better army than that which fought for the late Czar. There has been progress in the military art. In China we have seen not only the growth of a national spirit, but, under the influence of a lady whose name I shall not venture to pronounce, the inculcation of public morality and the social virtues. As for America, that has developed from a dissident coterie of ill-advised but worse-conducted savages——

LINCOLN

My dear Doctor ! The fathers of my country are venerated, at least in the United States, not only for the integrity of their minds, but their political acumen.

JOHNSON

They lived as near neighbours to the savages, and were infected by their perpetual dissension. But their descendants are better men. They have fostered the growth of learning, and raised the price of authorship. I repeat, sir, that of America to-day I have formed a high opinion.

LINCOLN

If I praise your candour, that will not imply agreement with the reasoning by which you have come to your good opinion. I hope you consider that Britain has made equal improvement on the accomplishments of *your* Eighteenth Century ?

JOHNSON

No, sir, in my own countrymen there has been less advancement. They have neglected their religion and forgotten how to write. They have no painter equal to Reynolds, nor an actor who could hold a candle to Davy Garrick. In certain directions they have gone downhill. But they are better than they were a few years ago, when they were little removed from being contemptible. They have come out of the doldrums, sir. They have shown hardihood and resolve, and now in several particulars are revealing a tincture of good sense. I have my hopes of England.

SOCRATES

If there has been this improvement in the countries you mention, and doubtless in others, is it not likely that their inhabitants are aware of national progress, and take pride in it ?

JOHNSON

It is very likely, sir.

SOCRATES

Then the reason for their fighting in this war may be national pride or patriotism?

JOHNSON

I would trust no one, sir, who gave such a reason. I have said it before, and I shall say it again, that patriotism is too often the last refuge of a scoundrel.

VOLTAIRE

Not his last refuge. His last refuge is to make a commodity of his country, and sell it.

LINCOLN

I never thought an epigram worth much as evidence, but it doesn't entitle one to throw the witness out of court. I would have said myself

76

that patriotism was still a very compulsive force, and where it happens to co-operate with the principles of good government, I cannot suppose it to be a despicable force. But young Arden, of whom I spoke to you before, tells me that people nowadays want a larger purpose. So both young and old, it may be, have agreed to discount it as a *casus belli*.

SOCRATES

Then we have still to find the reason why forty million men are at present using all their strength and ingenuity to kill each other. I wish it were possible to put some questions to an intelligent German or Japanese. But there are obvious difficulties.

LINCOLN

I was talking to Beethoven the other day — he's still asleep, is he ?

VOLTAIRE

Very soundly. It is only when sleep has locked both eyes and ears that a man will open his mouth so trustfully.

77

LINCOLN

I was talking to him, very gently and tactfully as I thought, about affairs in Germany, but he behaved like I'd been asking the price of rope of a man who'd had a lynching in the family.

VOLTAIRE

He once told me that he had forgotten the sound of his own language.

LINCOLN

You certainly don't hear it much around here.

VOLTAIRE

I encountered, recently, one of those early Teutons of the Heroic Age, Sigurd the Volsung. He also was quite unhelpful about modern Germany. When I asked him his opinion of the Aryan Theory, he proceeded to recite the pedigree of a stallion he had once owned, and finally it became apparent that in his time — the Fifth Century, I believe — the only recognised Aryan stock was a breed of small but sturdy horses.

LINCOLN

If I remember the story of Sigurd, he did his fighting with the simple object of getting rich, and because there was nothing else he could do without making a fool of himself. And that, as a motive, has gone out of fashion ; except in Germany. — But who's coming ? Are we going to have company ?

Voices are heard, growing louder as the speakers come near. They are two soldiers, both wearing tropical uniform, tattered and stained, and bleached by the sun. They pass the loggia, on a little road below the balustrade, paying no attention to the Immortals, but still talking loudly. They are tall and redoubtable figures, the one a SERGEANT *in the United States' Marine Corps, the other a* PIPER *of the Argyll and Sutherland Highlanders ; under his arm he is carrying a shabby-looking stand of pipes. Walking beside them, and listening to their argument, is* FLYING OFFICER ARDEN.

SERGEANT

Yes, sir. It was ignorance and lack of vision were to blame. We were caught with our trousers down, and why? On account of us having neither knowledge nor imagination.

PIPER

The very same with our Government ! What did they do about Singapore? Put a couple of fifteen-inch guns at the front gate, and left the back door unlocked. They never thought Japan would have the bad manners to come that way. They'd always gone to the front door themselves, and they thought Japan would do the same, and wipe its feet on the mat, and ring the bell to tell us it was there. It was just as you say, Sergeant : ignorance, and lack of imagination !

SERGEANT

That's what killed us, buddy : ignorance and stupidity. Well, what the hell !

Sings : ' From the halls of Montezuma
　　　　　To the shores of Tripoli,

We'll fight our country's battles
   On the land as on the sea . . .'

*Their voices, as they pass, grow smaller and fade into
silence.* ARDEN *leaves them and comes into the club.*

VOLTAIRE

How refreshing to hear men who take such a
realistic view of their world ! Who are they ?

LINCOLN

One is a Sergeant of our Marine Corps, but I
don't know the other.—Well, Arden, what have
you been doing ?

ARDEN

Good evening, sir. I was talking to some of the
soldiers in the Transit Camp, and then I walked up
the hill with two of them.

VOLTAIRE

Could you persuade them to return ? I should
like to make their acquaintance.

81

ARDEN

Yes, I'll bring them back. You really want to speak to them ?

VOLTAIRE

Of course.

ARDEN

You'll like them, I think.

He runs down the steps of the loggia.

VOLTAIRE

Socrates, you must certainly question these men. They are honest fellows, I am sure, and what is more, intelligent.

SOCRATES

If they help us in our enquiry, we shall certainly be indebted to them.

JOHNSON

Are there many soldiers in the Transit Camp, Mr. President ?

LINCOLN

The number varies from day to day. Our Records Office, unfortunately, is very much over-worked at present, and it takes some little time to get all the necessary details . . .

ARDEN *returns with the two soldiers.*

ARDEN

Here they are, sir.

LINCOLN

Come and sit down, Sergeant. There's a chair right here.

SERGEANT

Thank you, sir.

ARDEN

Here's another for you, Piper.

JOHNSON

From the evidence you carry, I take it that you are a Scotsman ?

PIPER

Yes, sir.

JOHNSON

Then pray, sir, make yourself as comfortable as you can. I was very hospitably received in your country, when I travelled there with a compatriot of yours, Mr. Boswell of Auchinleck.

PIPER

Indeed, sir ?

LINCOLN

I would appreciate it, Sergeant, if you were to tell these gentlemen the story you told me yesterday. It will bear repetition, have no fear of that. — The Sergeant, gentlemen, was one of the little garrison that defended Wake Island, last winter, with such notable resolution.

JOHNSON

Pray, sir, where is Wake Island ?

SERGEANT

In the Pacific Ocean, sir, about two thousand miles from Hawaii, on the direct route to Hong Kong.

JOHNSON

Can you describe it for us ?

SERGEANT

Well, it isn't much to look at, and you wouldn't choose it for a health resort. The whole area's no more than a square mile, and the maximum height above sea-level is eight feet. There's heavy brush to the eastward, growing fifteen feet or thereabout. The shape of the island is something like an Indian arrow-head, with two smaller islands on the wings, that partly enclose a lagoon full of coral reefs and fish. We were pretty glad of the fish.

JOHNSON

A very compendious description, sir.

LINCOLN

A speck in the ocean. Little, and lonely, and ill-fortified. And so low in the water. Why, when a storm was blowing, the whole island must have been awash.

SERGEANT

Yes, sir ! It got pretty nearly as wet as a battle-ship in a gale of wind. But we'd have held it all right if we'd gotten the defences finished in time. We weren't ready for them, that was the trouble. There were six or seven hundred contract labourers on the island when the Japs came. They'd been working well enough, but they hadn't hardly started. Then the Japs arrived with their battle-fleet and a flock of bombers like you see gulls over a dead whale, and beat the tar out of us. There were times when you thought they'd crack the island wide open, and sink it. You get a heavy salvo, and there's lumps of coral flying up, and chunks of coral coming down, and sand so as you can't see a yard in front of you, and then the brush goes on fire. Maybe the bombardment would quieten down at times, but it just started again like some guy had slipped another nickel in the juke-box. But they didn't do that for nothing. No, sir ! We gave 'em plenty. We sank a cruiser and spoiled the look of two or three others. We sank a destroyer and a submarine and shot down twelve of their planes for certain, and maybe more.

LINCOLN

That was with a garrison of four hundred men ?

SERGEANT

Yes, sir. I reckon there must have been nearly four hundred of us.

LINCOLN

And you kept up your defence, against all odds and expectation, for more than two weeks ?

SERGEANT

Sixteen days, sir.

JOHNSON

Sir, they were days which all Christendom should remember.

SERGEANT

It's kind of a pity they were wasted, but that's the way things go when you aren't ready. — How about your Malayan jungle, Jock ? That worth remembering ?

PIPER

I wouldna say it was worth remembering, but it'll take a big lot of forgetting. All that fighting for nothing ! Down through those rubber trees, and the sweat running off you like rain off a roof. Everything we wore was just rotted with sweat. And the Japs coming out of the trees like something out of a nightmare. They got round behind us. They came in ashore among the mangrove swamps, and when we'd beaten off an attack in front, there'd be more of them waiting behind. But there were a lot fewer when we'd finished. Then we got down to the butt-end of the peninsula, and we were the rear-guard. All that was left of the others crossed over the causeway into Singapore island, and we held the last position. There weren't so many of us either, but we'd done a good job till then, and we'd nothing to be ashamed of. There's many an army had to retreat, and a good retreat, a weel-fought retreat, is no disgrace to anyone, especially among rubber trees. — I never want to see another rubber tree as long as I live. — But then came our turn to go, and we marched onto the causeway, on a dark night full of the stink of mangroves and burning houses, with the pipes playing. But after that it wasna so good. After that it was hellish. I'm no going to talk about it. It's bad enough when you have to think, for it was just a calamity.

SOCRATES

And who, in your opinion, was responsible for the disaster?

PIPER

Who else but the Government? They hadna taken the trouble to learn what was what, and think clearly, and make proper plans. That was the whole reason.

SOCRATES

And do you, Sergeant, blame your Government for the failure to fortify your little island in the Pacific ?

SERGEANT

Well, we ought to have been ready for the Japs, and we weren't. And if you can't blame the Government, who can you ?

SOCRATES

It seems to me that both of you are right, and your Governments indeed are culpable. The first duty of a government is to secure the safety of its people and all their interests. If it fails to do this, it has failed in everything.

PIPER

It's the politicians are to blame. I wouldna trust a politician.

SOCRATES

But you do not, of course, condemn either people or institutions for a single mistake. It may be, for all I know, that with the exception of these recent blunders your Governments have behaved, for a long time, with faultless wisdom.

SERGEANT

It was Big Business in the United States that sold Japan most of its armament. Till the summer of 1941 they were getting their automobiles and gasoline and airplanes and scrap-iron direct from us, and the bombs that fell on Honolulu, a few months later, were made of good American metal. That doesn't smell of wisdom, unless my nose is out of joint. And though the United States is naturally the richest country in the world, for years before the war it was stinking with poverty. That's not an advertisement for faultless wisdom, is it ?

PIPER

It was the same with us, just the same. There were about three million on the dole in Britain at one time.   And our foreign policy was more bankrupt than that.

SOCRATES

But both your countries are democracies, are they not ?

SERGEANT

They certainly are. We don't want any of your kings and emperors in the United States.

PIPER

No more than we want a dictator in Britain. Democracy's good enough for us.

SOCRATES

And since they are democracies, your Governments do not merely represent the people, but *are* the people.   They are a concentration of the popular mind.   And if, as you seem to think, they have been guilty of criminal negligence, there must be some grave fault, not merely in your ministers, but in your whole population.

PIPER

There's been something wrong somewhere.

SOCRATES

Then why have you been fighting, with resolution as it appears, and probably with gallantry, for countries which are clearly unworthy of you ?

SERGEANT

Say, Mister, what are you getting at ?

SOCRATES

I am trying to find the reason for your going to war in the service of two nations whose people, on your own admission, are negligent and slothful ; and whose rulers, apparently unfitted for their task, cannot deserve your confidence.

PIPER

What's confidence got to do with it ? It's a poor sort of man that only bets on a certainty.

SOCRATES

In what way is he poor? Is he not richer in common sense than a man who will stake all he has — that is to say, his life — on a wrestler who has not trained for the fight?

SERGEANT

Now listen! I'm an American citizen, and as such I'm entitled to say exactly what I please about any Senator or Congressman that ever went to Washington. But when my country gets in a jam, I don't lie down and squeal, I start shooting. And why? Because I'm a man, not a rat. That's why.

PIPER

And that goes for me too.

SOCRATES

But if you are men, you should listen to reason, and I ask you again if it is reasonable to fight for an authority which, as you have stated, does not fulfil its obligations, and may be incapable of fulfilling them?

VOLTAIRE

Ignorance and stupidity, you said, were the cause of your death. Are you fighting to perpetuate ignorance and stupidity?

SERGEANT

If you two guys went around in some American city asking questions like that just for the hell of it, you'd wake up some morning cold and stiff and wonder what had hit you.

SOCRATES

That is almost exactly what did happen to me, a long time ago.

SERGEANT

Then it's a pity you didn't learn your lesson.

SOCRATES

How can a man learn anything except by asking questions of those who know?

PIPER

You might have learnt something, just by keeping your eyes open, if you'd been living in Central Europe for the last few years. You might have seen things that happen in German prison-camps, things that happen when the Gestapo comes around, and things that happened in Warsaw and that wee village in Czechoslovakia where they murdered every man and stamped the houses flat for the sheer lust of cruelty. And they're no new things either. They happened in the last war too. My old man was a sailor, and he was killed by a German submarine that torpedoed their ship and then came up and shelled an open boat. That's what Germany means, and that's what we're fighting against. And the defeat of Germany is cause enough for any man who just hopes to leave the world a place where his bairns can grow up in health and decency and some degree of safety.

SERGEANT

You might have learnt as much, or more, if you'd been in Nanking in 1938, when the Japs celebrated their victory with mass rape and murder.

I wasn't there, but my wife was. She was a nurse, and what she saw was enough to make any man get up and fight. The trouble was we didn't pay attention. They were Chinese that suffered, and I guess we thought it was none of our business what happened to them. But that's where we were wrong, and now we've learnt our mistake. My wife's a widow now, and she's got a child I've never seen. But if that child can live his life in a world where there's never another Nanking massacre, then I reckon we didn't waste our time on Wake Island.

SOCRATES

Your feelings do you a great deal of credit, and I sympathise with all you have said. But is there, in the present constitution of your countries, or anywhere upon earth, the promise or beginning of such a world-wide government as might bring to being the general security for which you hope? That offers, not only to your children but to the Chinese, a fuller and better life? If there is no such prospect, no widespread and explicit determination to organise a more sensible world, then it still seems to me that you have sacrificed your lives to no purpose.

SERGEANT

If you don't believe that Britain and the United States are in this God-damned war for a good reason, then nothing I can say will make any difference. Either you know, or you don't know, and that's all there is to it.

PIPER

He's only a foreigner, Sergeant. He canna understand.

SERGEANT

I guess that's so. Mr. Lincoln, sir, I'm sorry to find you in company like this. I've had enough of it, and if you take my advice, you won't share it much longer. — Come on, buddy, let's go. I like the Transit Camp better than this dump.

PIPER

I'm going to let them hear something first. — See you here, you in the blanket and you in the wig : when we gaed ower the causeway into that dismal and despairing island of Singapore, the wee Japs thought they had us fairly beat and finished. But we knew better. So we gave them a tune on the pipes that was mair than a tune, it was a promise we'd be back before long. And you're going to hear that same tune for a promise that when Great Britain and America stand on the one side together, it's bad policy to be on the other. Because we ken what's right and we ken what's wrong, me and the Sergeant, and there's a difference between them that nothing can hide. Not even your argument. Now just you wait . . .

SERGEANT

Let 'em have it, Jock. Mr. Lincoln, sir, you better clear out same as we're doing. The hell with civilians anyway . . .

The SERGEANT'S *further comment is luckily drowned in the din of pipes, for the* PIPER, *whose last words were intermitted with audible puffing as he filled his bag, is playing his regimental march :* Hielan' Laddie. *For a few seconds the noise is almost deafening, but it dwindles rapidly as he and the* SERGEANT *march back to their camp.*

LINCOLN

Socrates, those men made me feel a low-down ordinary creature.

SOCRATES

I was often put to shame by the natural honesty of the carpenters and stone-masons with whom I used to spend so much of my time in Athens. But to persuade a good man to think about the roots of his belief does him no harm. Indeed, it will make him a better man.

The PIPER'S *tune has awakened* BEETHOVEN, *and seemingly to no agreeable mood. For his voice is surly.*

BEETHOVEN

What made that noise ?

LINCOLN

A Scottish bagpipe.

BEETHOVEN

Only one ? Thank God there were no more. —
They say the Scots are good fighters.

JOHNSON

They have a reputation, sir, for aptitude in war.

BEETHOVEN

They must be very good fighters if their more
civilized neighbours cannot prevent them playing
such an infernal instrument as that. What was a
Scotsman doing here ?

LINCOLN

We were discussing with him why men go to
war.

BEETHOVEN

Because they are fools. Man is two things : he
is a fighting animal and a suffering animal. Suffer-

ing is a great part of our estate. But the majority are such fools that they don't try to heal their suffering, but to escape from it. They are such dreadful fools that to escape from normal suffering they will jump out of the frying-pan into the fire. That is to say, out of peace into war. — Can anyone tell me what's the time in Chicago?

LINCOLN

Chicago?

BEETHOVEN

I want to hear a concert there.

ARDEN

There's a universal clock behind you, sir. — It's a quarter to nine in Chicago.

BEETHOVEN

Then I can have another nap. I've been walking on the hills all day, and I'm tired.

He yawns, noisily, and settles himself to sleep again.

LINCOLN

There is more in it than folly.

JOHNSON

Yes, sir, there is a great deal more. Those two soldiers were honest men, and the Scotsman showed the bare bone of their honesty when he said they knew the difference between right and wrong. That, sir, is the ultimate categorical distinction.

VOLTAIRE

I was disappointed in them. I had thought, from their first words, they took a realistic view of the world, and were capable of reason. But no. They are still subject to their tribal superstitions and local prejudice. They belong to the majority.

JOHNSON

Then, sir, I must think better of the majority. You do well to exalt the place of reason, for reason is perpetually being brought down by our baser parts. But in the moral sphere reason has two champions, and you have forgotten one of them. There is ratiocination, but there is also conscience. In a free man, whose mind has neither been corroded by injurious circumstance nor corrupted with pernicious doctrine, there is a free and vocal conscience. And those two soldiers, the American and the Scotsman, were speaking, sir, with the voice of conscience.

LINCOLN

They are good men, both of them.

SOCRATES

They know what they are fighting against. They have made so much clear. But I am still perplexed by the enormity of the war, and it does not really help me to know that Voltaire and the Sergeant, who so dislike each other, are in perfect though limited agreement about their immediate enemy.

VOLTAIRE

I discovered, many years ago, how impossible it

was for a reasonable man to live within the personal dominion of a German autocrat. My poor dear Frederick, though his intentions were good, made life intolerable. And the Germans of to-day are infinitely worse than poor Frederick. He did try to improve a single mind — his own — but the Nazis, with greater zeal and more success, have undertaken the corruption of eighty million minds. Their manners are atrocious, their morals perverted, and their superstitions bestial. Yes, they are certainly the immediate enemy.

SOCRATES

It is, of course, far easier to recognise what is wrong than to envisage what is right. Especially in politics. Now the Allied nations, being in agreement about whom they are fighting against, will probably win the war. But unless they are in equal agreement about the cause they are fighting for, they will not be able to make a good and fruitful peace. And I ask you yet again : are they in agreement ? Does a positive cause yet exist ? Lincoln has said that some people, perhaps many, hope to see a rule of law established and enforced by Great Britain, America, Russia, and China. That, I believe, would be a good thing. It is fairly clear that Germany and Japan will never respect anything but a strength much greater than their own. And therefore, when you have beaten them, you can make sure of peace only by exterminating them, or creating such a strength as they cannot fail to acknowledge. And as you will not exterminate them, because it is not in your nature to do such a thing, you should, I think, create your fourfold rule of law.

But that, of itself, will not solve all your problems. A rule of law is only, as it were, the roof and walls of a temple. What makes a temple useful and significant is the sort of worship that is practised there. Are your people, when they have built their walls upon those cornerstones, going to worship what is good, and only what is good? They desire peace, but to be fruitful, peace must be married to justice. Now have your Allies made their minds clear about the decrees and temper of their justice? Those men who have died, your American Sergeant and your Scottish Piper, want their children to be given a better chance than they had of living freely and fully, with security in their own homes and with goodwill in their hearts. But if that is to come about there must be a sufficiency of men who are already determined to bring it about, and know how to begin. Are there such men? Men who are not self-seeking, but desire the good of others. Do they see clearly what a good world would be like, and are they strong enough, in love and resolution, to set to work?

LINCOLN

In the heat of conflict, when all their energy is concentrated on the earliest possible defeat of the enemy, our people can hardly sit down to make detailed plans for the future.

SOCRATES

It is only when his fire is hot that the blacksmith can give its shape to the weapon he is making. Either the war is a mere struggle for survival, like the fighting of animals, or it is creative. But if the Allies do not know what they are trying to make, they will waste both time and metal.

ARDEN

When you were alive, Socrates, you were a soldier yourself. You fought in several campaigns.

SOCRATES

Yes, I fought in the infantry.

ARDEN

Why?

SOCRATES

Now you are turning the tables on me. Well, my answer is that I fought for Athens.

ARDEN

Is that a sufficient answer?

SOCRATES

I was an Athenian citizen. My body, which had been nourished by Athens, belonged to Athens and therefore I could not honestly withhold it from her service. And my mind, which was free, I freely gave to Athens.

ARDEN

But you have not told us why.

SOCRATES

If you had known Athens, you would know the answer. . . . There was one of our sailors who had been to the Persian sea, where they fish for pearls, and there he had once seen a diver with a great pearl in either hand, which he held for display in the sunlight, and his face wore a look of almost heavenly joy, because he delighted equally in his strength and his good fortune. That was how Athens looked. The best of the Athenians were humanity in its most sinewy exaltation. High courage and lofty intelligence went hand-in-hand through the market-place. We did not copy our neighbour-states, but were an example to them. We were a democracy, but though all enjoyed an equal justice, the claim of excellence was quickly recognised. Unconstrained in our private intercourse, we showed always a reverence for authority and law, and while no one escaped labour, there was relaxation for all. We met danger with a light heart. We were lovers of the beautiful, yet simple in our tastes, and we cultivated the mind without loss of manliness. Wealth was not employed for ostentation, but in a sensible way, and though there was no disgrace in poverty, it was thought disgraceful if a man did nothing to avoid poverty. Nor did an Athenian citizen neglect the state because he had to take care of his household. We discussed everything, fully and freely, and we did not believe that discussion was an impediment to action. The great impediment, in our opinion, was the want of that knowledge which is gained by discussion. Athens was the school of all Hellas, and in the hour of trial Athens, alone among her contemporary states, showed herself not merely equal, but superior to her reputation. . . . When the sailor, coming home from the Persian sea, turned the point of Sunium, he saw glittering in the tall sky over the Acropolis the tip of Athene's spear, and by that alone, he said, he was assured of happiness when he went ashore. Like the diver he had seen, Athens was holding pearls in her grasp, and such a life as I have told but a fragment of its worth.

JOHNSON

And yet, sir, those same Athenians condemned you to your death.

SOCRATES

That was in the time of their defeat, when they could not look upon the truth.

ARDEN

Socrates . . . don't you think it may be a sort of omen that Greece was the first of the Allied nations to win a victory ? When Mussolini threw those stuffed divisions of his into Albania, Greece came to life again in the old way. There was that fearful campaign in the mountains, and the Italians were defeated. It was the Greeks who opened the scoring for us. I was dead by then, of course, but I remember watching the world, and everywhere on our side you could see men draw breath again, as if they too had come to life. There was some quality in the Greek army, in the people of Greece, that was more than ordinary courage and determination. It was like a religion. I suppose it was a religion. The old religion that made Athene, the goddess of wisdom, a warrior-goddess. And from that time, the time of the taking of Argyrokastro and Koritsa, you could see in England the waking of a new confidence. The English had made up their minds to go down fighting, if they had to go down — you remember the joke we made after Dunkirk, *We've got into the final now* — but then, when Greece began to fight, they saw the glint of victory, as if, like your sailor, they had seen the light on Athene's spear.

VOLTAIRE

The English, my dear Arden, are unlikely to have seen any such thing. You are suggesting, of course, that when England and her friends have won the war, they will create a new age of enlightened humanism like the inspired and eager liberalism of Athens in the time of Pericles. But no, my friend, no. The English are too fond of horses. In the old fable, you remember, Athene and Poseidon were in competition for the possession of Athens, and it was decided by the gods that whichever invented the most useful addition to human life should win the prize. Thereupon Poseidon produced a horse, and Athene planted an olive tree. The gods gave Athene the award, but had they been Englishmen, can you doubt that Poseidon would have got it?

JOHNSON

Sir, the English have now transferred their affection from horses to machinery.

VOLTAIRE

You astonish me, sir. Yet they have always been notorious for eccentricity, and they are, in addition, capable of seeing where advantage lies. — Arden, I may have to modify my previous opinion. Could your fellow-countrymen perceive that an age of enlightenment would truly profit them, they might set about establishing it. But you would have to convince them that the light on Athene's spear was the glitter of pure gold.

ARDEN

Convince them, you mean, that a guaranteed peace would be worth while ? That a world where everyone could fill his mind and his stomach, and hear the truth and rely on justice, would be better than a world of insecurity and hunger and fear ? Do they need to be convinced of that ? Doesn't common sense tell them so ?

VOLTAIRE

Come, come, my dear boy, that is dangerous talk. To propose governing the world by good sense is to preach the most drastic form of revolution. Only an Englishman would dare suggest it, for only the English will tolerate the very excesses of free thinking.

ARDEN

But everyone of my age knows, and says it openly, that there must be more common sense in government. More understanding and a better vision. The world was only a jungle to begin with, but men — our sort of men — made it fit to live in.

And if they have done so much, they can do more. And they're going to !

VOLTAIRE

Your young men, I hope, will not be too impatient. They must remember, for one thing, that the English have always hated compulsion, and therefore it would be impolitic to force them into good sense, for fear they turn against it, as if it were another Germany. You should rather plant your seeds of enlightenment quite furtively, and let them grow at first in seclusion, and then apparently in defiance of authority. By such means you will make them popular, and authority itself may welcome the appearance of novelties which it would have liked to sow by Act of Parliament, but dared not lest the people suspected it of tyranny. It would be useful to begin your campaign in a few selected schools. There are so many varieties of school in England that no one can possibly know what is going on there.

ARDEN

My brother is a schoolmaster. Or he was,

before the war, He's a soldier now, somewhere in the Western Desert. He got the sack from one school when he told the Head that his system of teaching was worthless, because he had never discovered the difference between education and instruction.

VOLTAIRE

An excellent young man. A soldier, you say? A General, I must suppose.

ARDEN

No, he's a Sergeant.

VOLTAIRE

Let us hope he will become a General very soon. How right he was to insist on such a vital difference! For instruction teaches us to work, which is necessary, but education how to live, which ought to be delicious. They are, I am told, about to extend the school-age in England. They will extend it to seventy, I hope. And your brother was discharged, you say?

ARDEN

But a month later he got a better job in a bigger school.

VOLTAIRE

Now there you see the benevolence and breadth of English life and the English mind ! They are elastic, not rigid. When you abolished the tyranny of kingship, you also destroyed the despotism of uniformity. Almost do I begin to share your confidence, Arden. When I lived in England I knew Pope, and Swift, and Congreve. The good Berkeley was preaching and philosophising, Newton was still alive, and in the London taverns you could see their compatriots, men broadly built, red-faced, untouched by any thought — you would say — except of the beer and beefsteak pudding which they digested with such prodigious appetite. Yes, in that soil it is possible that anything may grow. Anything at all. Even good.

JOHNSON

Sir, you are right. A great deal of good has

grown there, and I doubt not that more is already sprouting. But, sir, we have explored a broad expanse of ocean, have we yet found any dry land ? Has Socrates yet satisfied himself that we are fighting this war for a sufficient purpose ?

SOCRATES

I see upon the horizon a kind of cloud, which is lighted by Arden's faith and the honesty of the two soldiers. It may, indeed, be something more solid than a cloud.

LINCOLN

I pray it is. There was never a sailor, starving and benighted on the open sea, who prayed more fervently for a good landfall than I pray now that our forces may have speedy victory, and good fruits of their victory . . .

He is interrupted by the noise of an undisguised and hearty yawn. BEETHOVEN *has wakened again.*

BEETHOVEN

Young man, what time is it in Chicago ?

ARDEN

A minute to nine, sir.

BEETHOVEN

Then let us have some music.

He rises from his chair and walks heavily to the television set. Presently the screen is lighted, and a swarm of images — like a drop of pond water under a microscope — appear momentarily, and disappear, as BEETHOVEN *searches for the scene he wants.*

BEETHOVEN

What have you been talking about ?

LINCOLN

War and peace.

BEETHOVEN

Are they going to make a good peace ?

JOHNSON

Sir, we hope so . . .

A picture appears on the screen of a symphony orchestra : fiddle-bows flashing like a flight of arrows in the sun, wood-winds and brass at work, and a tall, grey-haired conductor driving them, as if to the attack, with precise but exultant gestures. DR. JOHNSON *is interrupted.*

BEETHOVEN

Confound that clock, it's slow again ! My Symphony's half done, three-quarters done, they're near the end of it. The devil take all clocks, they're always slow . . .

He is silenced, abruptly, by the full voice of the orchestra. They are playing his Seventh Symphony, and they have newly begun the fourth movement. The Immortals listen for a little while, and then BEETHOVEN *speaks, while the music continues.*

BEETHOVEN

You have been talking about war and the making of peace. Well, that is the peace I made. I had been at war like the rest of the world. But I was alone in my war, I had no allies. I knew all the anguish and disillusion that man is heir to. But I took arms against them, and in the heart of the conflict saw the peace that I should make. Do not think peace to be a shallow or a placid thing. It is deep and rich. It is full of movement and joy, of work and laughter and the reaching-out of your hands to God. That is the peace of a living soul. Have nothing to do with any thin or idle peace, mere rest from toil and relapse from war. That is only the peace of dying. Listen. . . . There is a just and proper peace, and I saw it in the thick of battle. Will they make as good a one, d'you think ?

LINCOLN

You set too high a standard.

BEETHOVEN

I was alone, but they are many. If they put all their minds together, will the sum not equal mine in desire, and vision, and determination ? That is the creative trinity : desire, and vision, and deter-mination.

The music continues.

Printed in Great Britain by R. & R. CLARK, LIMITED, *Edinburgh*